GREAT SHOWSTOPPERS

WISE PUBLICATIONS
PART OF THE MUSIC SALES GROUP
LONDON / NEW YORK / PARIS / SYDNEY / COPENHAGEN / BERLIN / MADRID / TOKYO

GREAT SHOWSTOPPERS

ALL I ASK OF YOU THE PHANTOM OF THE OPERA 8

ALMOST PARADISE FOOTLOOSE THE MUSICAL 10

ANY DREAM WILL DO JOSEPH AND THE AMAZING

TECHNICOLOR® DREAMCOAT 12

AS LONG AS HE NEEDS ME OLIVER! 14

CAN YOU FEEL THE LOVE TONIGHT THE LION KING 16

CAN'T TAKE MY EYES OFF YOU JERSEY BOYS 18

CHIM CHIM CHER-EE MARY POPPINS 20

DEFYING GRAVITY WICKED 22

DO-RE-MI THE SOUND OF MUSIC 24

ELECTRICITY BILLY ELLIOT 26

I DREAMED A DREAM LES MISÉRABLES 5

(I'VE HAD) THE TIME OF MY LIFE DIRTY DANCING 28

MAMMA MIA! MAMMA MIA! 30

MAYBE THIS TIME CABARET 32

THE RHYTHM OF LIFE SWEET CHARITY 34

SEASONS OF LOVE RENT 40

UNDER PRESSURE WE WILL ROCK YOU 36

WE'RE ALL IN THIS TOGETHER HIGH SCHOOL MUSICAL ON STAGE 38

YOU CAN'T STOP THE BEAT HAIRSPRAY 43

YOU'RE THE ONE THAT I WANT GREASE 46

PUBLISHED BY
WISE PUBLICATIONS
14-15 BERNERS STREET, LONDON, W1T 3LJ, UK.

EXCLUSIVE DISTRIBUTORS:
MUSIC SALES LIMITED
DISTRIBUTION CENTRE, NEWMARKET ROAD, BURY ST EDMUNDS,
SUFFOLK, IP33 3YB, UK.
MUSIC SALES PTY LIMITED
20 RESOLUTION DRIVE, CARINGBAH, NSW 2229, AUSTRALIA.

ORDER NO. AM993355
ISBN 978-1-84772-530-1
THIS BOOK © COPYRIGHT 2009 BY WISE PUBLICATIONS,
A DIVISION OF MUSIC SALES LIMITED.

MUSIC ARRANGED BY ZOE BOLTON.
MUSIC PROCESSED BY PAUL EWERS MUSIC DESIGN.
EDITED BY FIONA BOLTON.
PRINTED IN THE EU.

YOUR GUARANTEE OF QUALITY
AS PUBLISHERS, WE STRIVE TO PRODUCE EVERY BOOK TO THE HIGHEST
COMMERCIAL STANDARDS. THE MUSIC HAS BEEN FRESHLY ENGRAVED AND
THE BOOK HAS BEEN CAREFULLY DESIGNED TO MINIMISE AWKWARD PAGE
TURNS AND TO MAKE PLAYING FROM IT A REAL PLEASURE.
PARTICULAR CARE HAS BEEN GIVEN TO SPECIFYING ACID-FREE, NEUTRAL-
SIZED PAPER MADE FROM PULPS WHICH HAVE NOT BEEN ELEMENTAL
CHLORINE BLEACHED. THIS PULP IS FROM FARMED SUSTAINABLE FORESTS
AND WAS PRODUCED WITH SPECIAL REGARD FOR THE ENVIRONMENT.
THROUGHOUT, THE PRINTING AND BINDING HAVE BEEN PLANNED TO
ENSURE A STURDY, ATTRACTIVE PUBLICATION WHICH SHOULD GIVE YEARS
OF ENJOYMENT. IF YOUR COPY FAILS TO MEET OUR HIGH STANDARDS,
PLEASE INFORM US AND WE WILL GLADLY REPLACE IT.

WWW.MUSICSALES.COM

I Dreamed A Dream

Music by Claude-Michel Schönberg
Original Lyrics by Alain Boublil & Jean-Marc Natel
English Lyrics by Herbert Kretzmer

Based on an 1862 novel by Victor Hugo, this musical was first staged in Paris in 1980. Abandoned by her lover, dismissed from her job and struggling to survive and support her daughter, Fantine, one of a cast of characters seeking liberation and revolution in early 19th-century France, sings about her broken dreams.

Hints & Tips: Notice how the melody is passed between the right and left hands in bars 9–14. Try to bring out the top note of the left-hand chords where they contain the melody note and create a smooth line between these parts.

as they tear your hope a - part, as they turn your dream to

shame.

mp And still I dreamed he'd come to me,

that we would live the years to - geth - er. But there are dreams that can - not

be,

and there are storms we can - not weath- er.

mf

I had a dream my life would be,

so diff -'rent from this hell I'm liv - ing; so diff-'rent now from what it

seemed.

Now life has killed the dream I dreamed.

mp

7

All I Ask Of You

Music by Andrew Lloyd Webber
Lyrics by Charles Hart
Additional Lyrics by Richard Stilgoe

This song was released as a single by Sarah Brightman and Cliff Richard in 1986, although it was Steve Barton who starred alongside her as Raoul when the show opened at Her Majesty's Theatre, London that year. Michael Crawford famously played The Phantom, a mysterious, disfigured musical genius in this production.

Hints & Tips: Create a legato feel to this piece by holding each note for its full length and joining it to the next as smoothly as possible even when there is a large interval to span (bars 9–16).

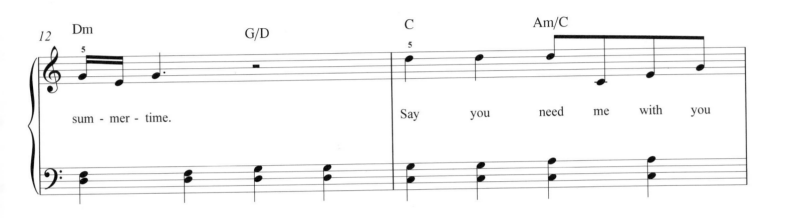

Almost Paradise

Words & Music by Dean Pitchford & Eric Carmen

This duet is the official love theme of the 1984 movie on which the show is based. It is sung by Ariel, daughter of the repressive Reverend Moore, and city boy Ren, who helps the small town Bomont recover from the memory of a tragic car accident by persuading them to reintroduce dancing after a five-year ban.

Hints & Tips: Pay careful attention to the fingering markings in this piece. There are some tricky corners in the right hand but following the recommendations should help you through these.

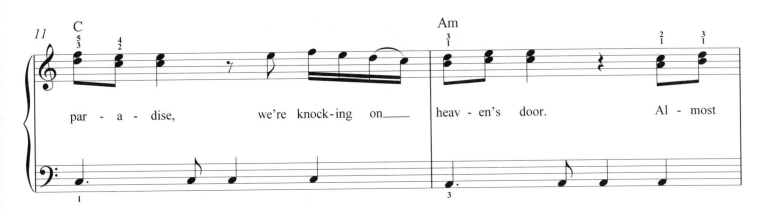

par - a - dise, we're knock-ing on___ heav - en's door. Al - most

par - a - dise, how could we ask for more? I

swear that I could see for - ev - er in your___ eyes. Par - a - dise.

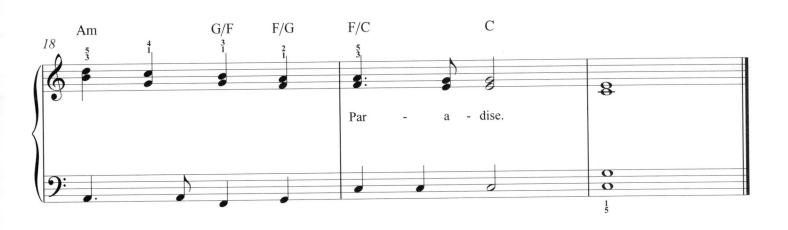

Par - a - dise.

Any Dream Will Do

Music by Andrew Lloyd Webber
Lyrics by Tim Rice

Released as a single in 1991 by Jason Donovan who was then playing Joseph in the West End production of the musical at the London Palladium, this song topped the UK charts for two weeks. In 2007 BBC TV ran a series, named after the song, searching for a new 'Joseph', a role eventually secured by Lee Mead.

Hints & Tips: Practise the left-hand part in the first 16 bars of this piece individually paying careful attention to the syncopated rhythm. Although it is a lively accompanying line, play it softly to ensure it doesn't drown out the melody. You should raise the dynamic of both hands in the chorus.

crash of drums,___ a flash of light,___ my gold - en coat,___ flew

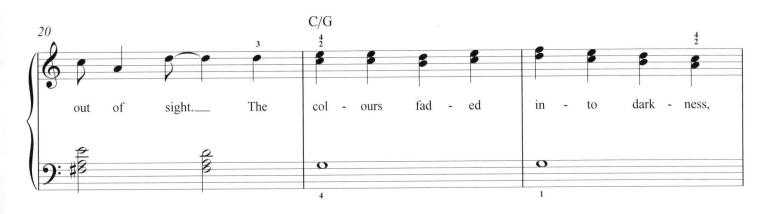

out of sight.___ The col - ours fad - ed in - to dark - ness,

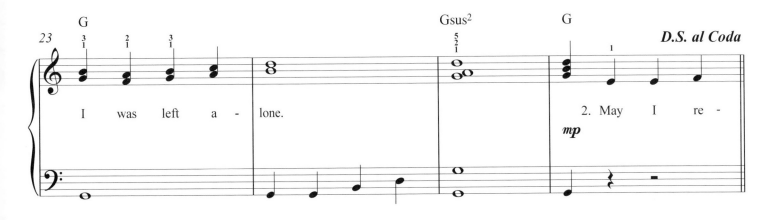

I was left a - lone. 2. May I re -

D.S. al Coda

𝄌 *Coda*

an - y dream will do.

As Long As He Needs Me

Words & Music by Lionel Bart

Possibly the most widely-recorded song from Lionel Bart's 1960 adaptation of the Charles Dickens novel *Oliver Twist*, 'As Long As He Needs Me' is sung as a love ballad by the character Nancy to her criminal boyfriend Bill Sikes. Sadly her love proves to be unrequited as he mistreats and subsequently murders her.

Hints & Tips: There are some interesting harmonies in this piece. Some of them might sound a little odd at first but play them confidently rather than shy away from them and they will sound much more convincing!

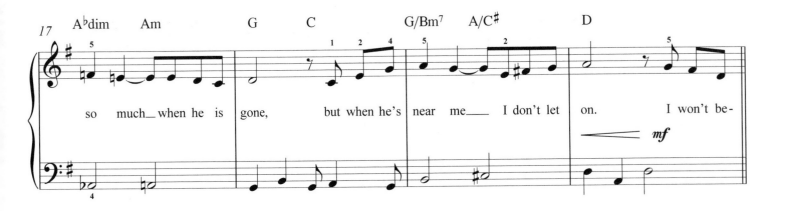

Can You Feel The Love Tonight

Words by Tim Rice
Music by Elton John

This musical, based on Disney's 1994 animated film and featuring actors in animal costumes and giant puppets, opened on Broadway in 1997 and in London's West End at the Lyceum Theatre in 1999. Performed by composer Elton John, this song won a Grammy Award for Best Male Pop Vocal Performance.

Hints & Tips: Listen carefully to the right hand in the chorus (from bar 9) to ensure the two notes are sounding at exactly the same time.

Can't Take My Eyes Off You

Words & Music by Bob Crewe & Bob Gaudio

This documentary-style musical, which opened on Broadway in November 2005 and at London's Prince Edward Theatre in February 2008, tells the turbulent story of the rise to fame of Frankie Valli and The Four Seasons, although this song from 1967 was one of several hits that Valli recorded without the group.

Hints & Tips: Watch out for the accidentals in this piece and remember that they apply to the entire bar in which they appear.

Chim Chim Cher-ee

Words & Music by Richard M. Sherman & Robert B. Sherman

Inspired by a drawing of a chimney sweep created by Mary Poppins' screenwriter Don DaGradi, and originally sung by Julie Andrews and Dick Van Dyke in the 1964 movie, this song won an Academy Award for Best Original Song. The stage musical premiered in London in 2004 and on Broadway two years later.

Hints & Tips: Place an emphasis on the first beat in each bar, especially in the left hand, to create a strong waltz feel to this jolly song.

Defying Gravity

Words & Music by Stephen Schwartz

This song is the finale for the first act of the show when the main character Elphaba discovers that The Wizard of Oz is not the heroic figure she had originally believed him to be and, vowing to do everything in her power to fight his sinister plans, escapes by flying away on a broomstick.

Hints & Tips: Although written almost entirely using crotchets and dotted minims, you can create a freer, more dramatic feel to this song by employing *rubato*; play some notes slightly longer than written but be sure to balance this out by making others slightly shorter—it's a case of 'give and take', or 'robbing' as the direct translation dictates.

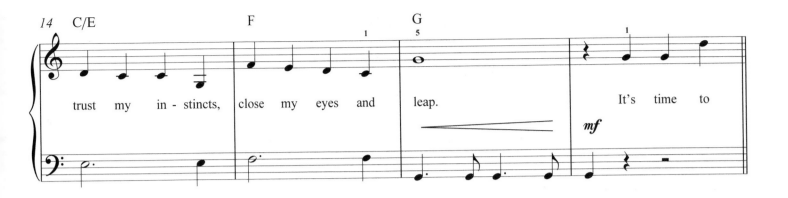

trust my in - stincts, close my eyes and leap. It's time to

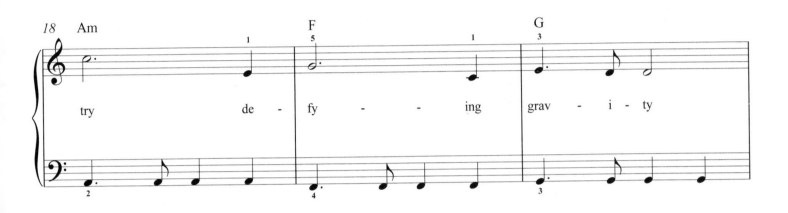

try de - fy - - ing grav - i - ty

I think I'll try de - fy - ing grav - i - ty, and

you can't pull me down._____

Do-Re-Mi

Words by Oscar Hammerstein II
Music by Richard Rodgers

This was the last musical written by Rodgers and Hammerstein as the latter died soon after its Broadway premiere in 1959. Shortly after being introduced to the Von Trapp children their governess, Maria, uses this song to teach them the notes of the musical scale as they learn to sing.

Hints & Tips: Rock gently between the two notes in the introduction if your left hand cannot reach to an octave. Keep your wrist loose and your touch light. If you're struggling omit the higher note.

Electricity

Words by Lee Hall
Music by Elton John

Set mainly in a north England mining town at the time of the 1980s coal miners' strike, this musical, scored by Elton John, revolves around motherless Billy and his personal struggle for fulfilment having traded boxing gloves for ballet shoes, balanced against a counter-story of family and community strife.

Hints & Tips: With three sharps in the key signature and a sprinkling of other accidentals in both hands you'll need to have your wits about you for the first nine bars. Try to look ahead as you're playing so they don't come as a surprise. After the key change it should be relatively plain sailing!

(I've Had) The Time Of My Life

Words & Music by Frankie Previte, John DeNicola & Donald Markowitz

Somewhat unusually the first stage adaptation of the 1987 film was produced in Australia in 2004. When, two years later, it opened at the Aldwych Theatre in the West End, it had the highest pre-sales in London history, not unsurprisingly, as the film's soundtrack is still one of the best-selling of all time.

Hints & Tips: Practise this song with a metronome to help you keep to a steady beat rather than rushing through the easier sections, especially where the style changes at bar 17.

Mamma Mia!

Words & Music by Benny Andersson, Stig Anderson & Björn Ulvaeus

This stage musical, which opened in London in 1999 and on Broadway in 2001, takes its title from Abba's second UK No. 1 hit. It topped the charts for two weeks early in 1976, nearly two months after its release, replacing Queen's 'Bohemian Rhapsody', another song which includes 'mamma mia' in its lyrics!

Hints & Tips: Keep the left-hand accompaniment light and place an emphasis on the first crotchet in each bar to avoid it sounding monotonous. This will also give the arrangement a stronger sense of pulse.

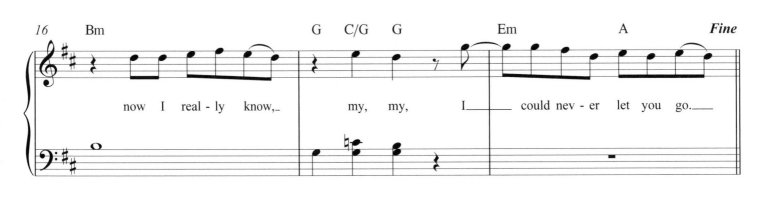

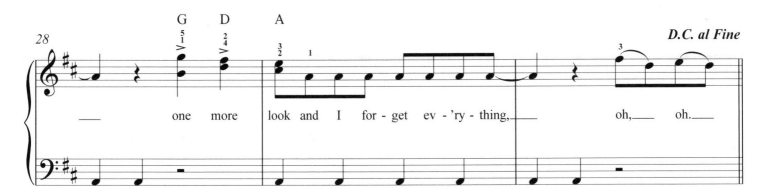

CABARET
Maybe This Time

Words by Fred Ebb
Music by John Kander

Written by the musical's composer John Kander for singer Kaye Ballard, although not included in the original 1966 Broadway production, this song was added to the 1972 film version and the 1998 Broadway revival, and has become a concert standard as performed by the likes of Liza Minnelli and Tony Bennett.

Hints & Tips: Avoid the left-hand chords sounding too heavy by placing a slight emphasis on the first beat of each bar and playing the remaining three crotchets more softly.

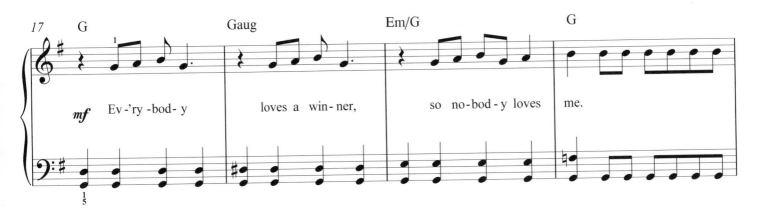

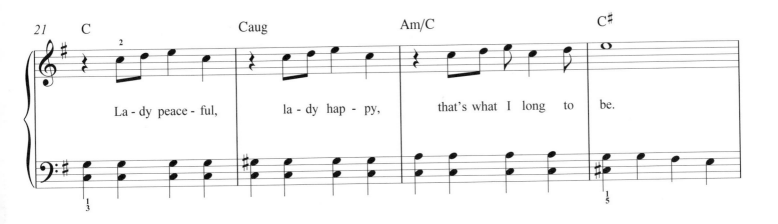

The Rhythm Of Life

Words by Dorothy Fields
Music by Cy Coleman

This musical, which opened on Broadway in 1966, follows the unlikely adventures of Charity Hope Valentine, a dancer at the Fandango Ballroom, New York, who gets stuck in a lift at the local YMCA with a claustrophobic accountant and is invited to his Rhythm Of Life Church.

Hints & Tips: Aim to play the quavers in this piece as evenly as possible. Practise playing them with a strict dotted rhythm adopting a dotted quaver-semiquaver pattern and then reversing this such that the pattern is semiquaver-dotted quaver.

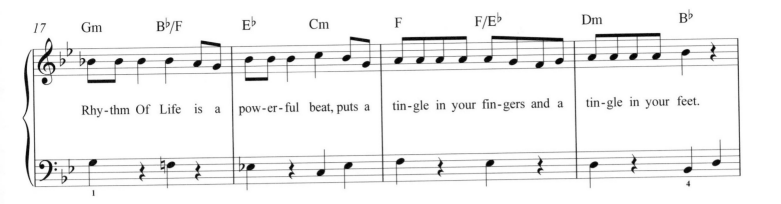

Rhy-thm Of Life is a pow-er-ful beat, puts a tin-gle in your fin-gers and a tin-gle in your feet.

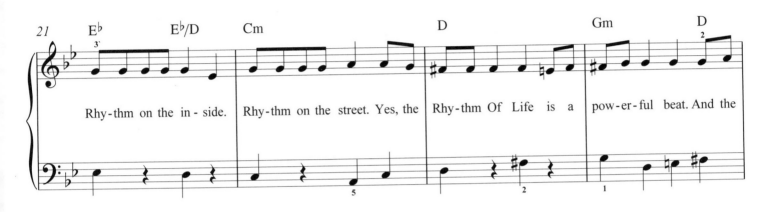

Rhy-thm on the in - side. Rhy-thm on the street. Yes, the Rhy-thm Of Life is a pow-er-ful beat. And the

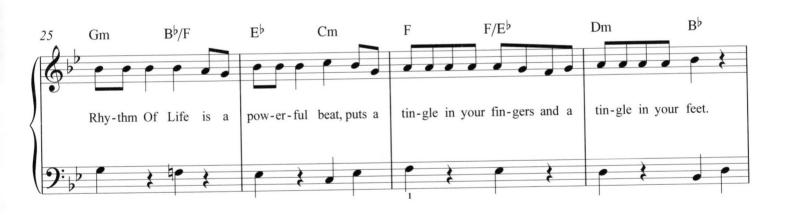

Rhy-thm Of Life is a pow-er-ful beat, puts a tin-gle in your fin-gers and a tin-gle in your feet.

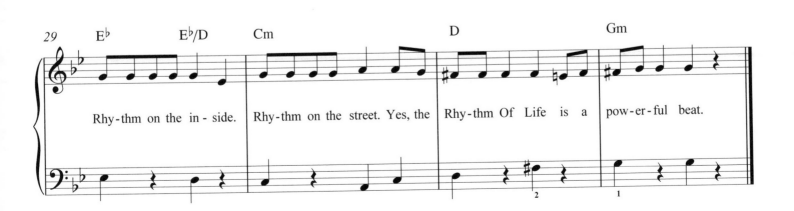

Rhy-thm on the in - side. Rhy-thm on the street. Yes, the Rhy-thm Of Life is a pow-er-ful beat.

WE WILL ROCK YOU

Under Pressure

Words & Music by David Bowie, Freddie Mercury, Roger Taylor, John Deacon & Brian May

Based on the songs of Queen, this musical was written by comedian and author Ben Elton along with band members Brian May and Roger Taylor, and is set in a future Orwellian world where musical instruments are forbidden and rock music is unknown.

Hints & Tips: Practise this piece under tempo at first, only increasing the speed once you have put the two hands together, and keeping your left-hand wrist loose to enable you to fit in the semiquavers without slowing back down.

We're All In This Together

Words & Music by Robbie Nevil & Matthew Gerrard

Having secured lead parts in the school winter musical, Troy and Gabriella celebrate victories in both the basketball championship and the scholastic decathlon alongside their fellow students at East High in this breathless finale to the Disney Channel smash hit musical.

Hints & Tips: Watch out for the two key signature changes in this piece as we move from F major, to G major and then A major. Mark in any accidentals that you are prone to forgetting.

Seasons Of Love

Words & Music by Jonathan Larson

Often associated with AIDS awareness campaigns because four of the lead characters are HIV postive, this song is performed by the entire cast of the rock opera, based on Puccini's *La Bohème*, as they suggest various ways of measuring a year, concluding that the only proper measure in a human life is love.

Hints & Tips: The first 16 bars of this piece feature a four-bar ostinato in the left hand. Observe the suggested fingering and practise this separately before putting the right-hand melody on top.

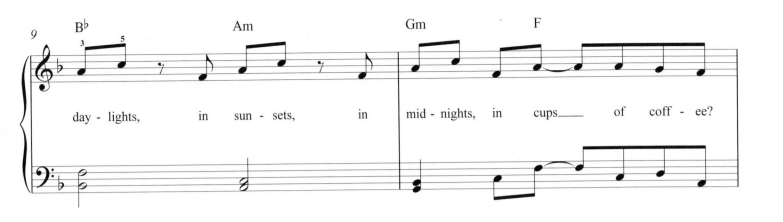

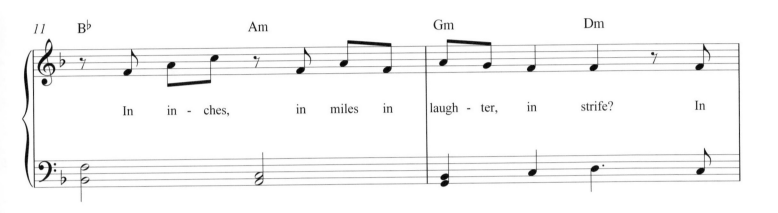

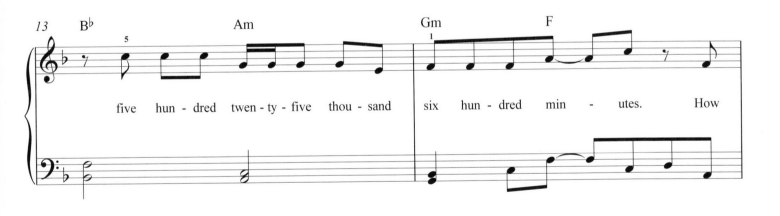

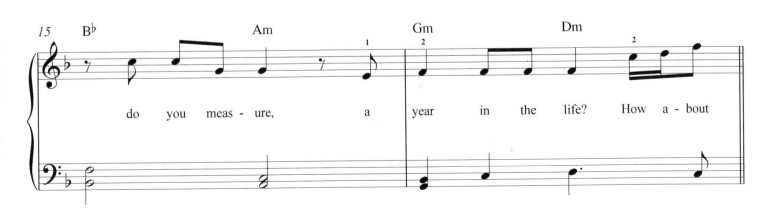

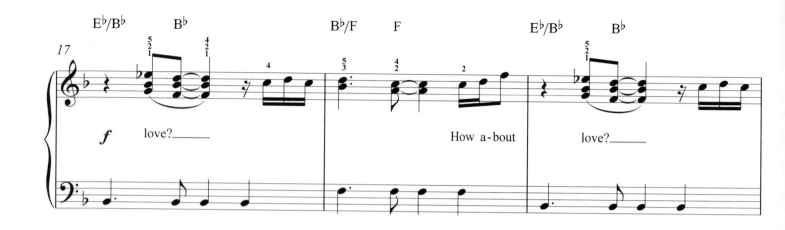

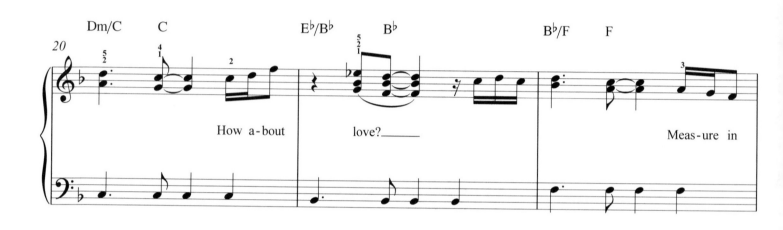

You Can't Stop The Beat

Words & Music by Marc Shaiman & Scott Wittman

First conceived as a stage musical after producer Margo Lion saw the original film on TV, a Broadway production opened in 2002 and won eight Tony Awards. The show debuted in London in 2007 gaining a record-setting eleven Olivier Award nominations, winning four categories including Best New Musical.

Hints & Tips: There is a lot of syncopation in this song, especially in bars 9–20. The steady left-hand crotchets should help to ground you, but mark in the crotchet beats with a line above the stave if this helps.

You're The One That I Want

Words & Music by John Farrar

Still one of the UK's best-selling singles having topped the charts on both sides of the Atlantic as recorded by John Travolta and Olivia Newton-John, this song was written for the 1978 film but didn't make it into the stage production until the revival of 2007!

Hints & Tips: Make sure you allow the rests in the left hand (of which there are many!) to last for their full value. It is easy to rush these gaps between notes so use a metronome to help you keep the tempo constant.